KU-225-973

Contents

The World of the Vikings' Tales

The Vikings were people who lived in Scandinavia around the years 700 to 1100. They believed in lots of different gods and other things like giants and dark elves, and told lots of tales about them.

The world the gods lived in was very different to our world. The Vikings believed that the gods and the people lived in a very big tree. The name of the tree was Yggdrasil.

At the top of the tree was Asgard, where the gods lived. In the middle of the tree was Midgard, where humans lived. At the bottom of the tree was Niflheim, where people went after they died. There was a big city in Niflheim. The name of this city was Hel.

There were other places too: Jotunheim, where the giants lived and Svartalfheim, where the dark elves lived.

There was a bridge between Asgard and Midgard. The name of this bridge was Bifrost, and it was like a burning rainbow. Sometimes the gods travelled over the bridge to Midgard, and met ordinary human people.

A very big snake, whose name was Jormungand, lived in the sea around Midgard. He was so big he made a circle around all of Midgard, and his tail met his mouth. A squirrel – Ratatosk – ran up and down the tree, taking messages from one world to another. An eagle and a hawk lived at the top of the tree, and the dragon Nidhogg lived at the bottom of it.

Odin was the chief of the gods. He lived in a big house in Asgard. The Vikings did not call these big houses 'palaces', they called them 'halls'. The name of Odin's hall was Valhalla. Every night, there was a big feast in Valhalla, with Odin and the souls of men who died fighting in battles. A feast was a very big meal, where everyone sat together and

The Vikings believed that the gods and the people lived in a very big tree. The name of the tree was Yggdrasil.

ate and drank a lot. Odin was very intelligent, but he also got angry quickly. He only had one eye, and always wore a big hat. Sometimes, when he went to Midgard, he used the hat to hide himself, or to pretend to be someone else. He always wore a blue cloak, and had a magic spear. Two ravens always sat on his shoulder.

Thor was the second most important Viking god. Thor was the son of Odin, and was the god of thunder and lightning. He was very tall, and had red hair and a big, red beard. Like his father, Thor also got angry very quickly. He was always very hungry, and ate two goats at every meal. Thor was not as intelligent as his father, but he was very strong and always told the truth. He had a magic hammer called Mjollnir. With Mjollnir, Thor could make thunder and lightning. He lived in Asgard, in a big palace named Bilskirnir. He often used his strength and his hammer to fight the giants who sometimes attacked Asgard.

Loki was another important god. Loki was a difficult god. Sometimes he was good, and sometimes he was bad. Sometimes he helped the other gods, and sometimes he made problems for them. He was very intelligent, and often played jokes or tricks on people or the other gods. He liked to make trouble for them – sometimes for fun, but other times because he was bad. Nobody ever knew what Loki was thinking, or what he was going to do. He could change shape, and become a fish, or an insect or sometimes a bird so he could travel very quickly.

Freyja was the most important goddess, the goddess of love. She was a very tall, very beautiful woman. When she cried, she cried tears of gold. She travelled in a chariot which was pulled by two cats.

There were many other gods too. There was Tyr, for example, who was the bravest of the gods – he was not afraid of anything. And there was Balder, who was the kindest and most handsome god.

The giants were the enemies of the gods. The giants were very, very big people. They were very strong. They were not all bad, but they loved to make problems for the gods.

The dark elves were not good, though. They were very clever at making beautiful jewellery and strong swords. But they were always greedy, and wanted lots of things for themselves. They were not friendly people. They only woke up at night, and if they saw the sun or the light of the day, they died.

A Picture Dictionary

helmet
spear
warrior
lightning
dragon
beard
castle
armour
cave
chariot
chain
cloak
glove
axe
hammer
sword
rainbow
squirrel
teeth
tail
goat
rope
snake
wolf

The People In The Stories

Odin,
the chief of the gods

Thor, Odin's son

Loki

Freyja

Tyr

The dark elf Alvis

The giant Thrym

Sigurd

Sigrdrifa

1

Fenrir's Chain

This is the story of Loki's children, and what happened to them. The god Loki had three children, but these were not ordinary children.

Loki's children were a snake whose name was Jormungand, a scary woman whose name was Hel, and a wolf whose name was Fenrir. At first they lived in Jotunheim, the country of the giants, but then they all came to Asgard, where the gods lived, and the gods were very worried.

'I don't like Loki's children!' said Odin, the most important of the gods. 'Loki is a dangerous man. He's always playing tricks. His children will be as dangerous as he is!'

The goddess Freyja did not think the same thing. 'But sometimes Loki is good,' she said. 'He has helped us lots of times. I think his children can live here in Asgard, with us.'

'But they're a snake, a strange-looking, scary woman and a wolf!' shouted Odin. 'They can't live here!'

Thor thought the same thing.

So first they took Jormungand the snake. Jormungand was so big the gods needed all the strength of Odin and Thor and two other gods, Tyr and Balder, to pick him up. Then, they threw him out of Asgard, which was at the top of the world, all the way down to Midgard. With a big, loud noise, the snake fell into the world of the humans. In Midgard, Jormungand started to grow and grow and grow. In the end, there was no space left for him there, so he went into the sea which was all around Midgard. When he was in the sea, he grew and grew until he made a circle around the entire world. His tail went into his mouth.

'Now then,' said Odin, 'What about Loki's daughter, Hel?'

The gods all looked at Hel, and even they were frightened. Her head was the head of a normal woman, but the rest of her body was like a skeleton, only bones and dead skin.

'I know what do with her,' said Odin, who was very clever. 'This woman is half-alive and half-dead. She can't live with us, because we're gods, and she can't live with the humans in Midgard, because she isn't human. We'll send her to Niflheim!'

'To Niflheim!' shouted Freyja. 'But that's a terrible place! That is the place where people go when they have died!'

'Exactly!' said Odin. 'Hel will be the best queen for Niflheim. I'll give her a city there, and the name of that city will be Hel, too!'

Because Odin was the most important god he always got what he wanted. So Hel was sent down to Niflheim where she became the queen of all the people who have died.

'So, then,' asked Thor, 'What are we going to do with this wolf?'

All of the gods – Odin and Thor and Freyja and Tyr and Balder looked at the wolf.

'A wolf is only a type of dog,' said Freyja.

'That's true,' said Thor. 'And if you're kind to a dog, the dog will grow up to be a good dog.'

'Perhaps that's true for wolves, as well,' said Freyja.

Again, all the gods looked at the wolf. It was only a baby wolf. It was beautiful, grey and white in colour, with blue eyes. He was quite a handsome wolf.

'You know what I think?' asked Thor.

'No – and I'm not sure I really *want* to know what you think!' said Odin slowly. Thor's father did not think his son was very intelligent.

'Tell us Thor!' said Tyr.

'I think he can live here,' said Thor. 'We've given homes

to Loki's other two children, and this one will be no trouble to us, the gods, here in our home.'

'Thor is right!' said Freyja.

'Very well then,' said Odin, 'The wolf can stay here!'

'Thank you!' said Fenrir – and the gods were all surprised that a wolf could talk! Everybody was very pleased. The gods played with the wolf like a dog. The god Tyr was his best friend, and they played together all the time.

At first, everything was fine. Fenrir the wolf lived in Asgard with the gods, and played in the big fields and gardens like an ordinary dog. But Fenrir was always very hungry. He ate and ate and ate and as he ate he got bigger and bigger and bigger. Often, when he was hungry, he started to get very angry.

The gods started to worry about this very big, hungry, angry wolf that lived with them.

'We need to tie him up!' said Thor.

'I think you're right!' said Odin.

So the gods found the biggest, strongest, thickest piece of rope they could find.

'Here, Fenrir!' they shouted to the wolf. 'We're going to tie you up so you can stay near us all the time!'

Fenrir did not like this. But he thought that if he was close to the gods, they would not leave him. He thought they would give him lots of food to eat. So he came closer to them.

When he was very close, Thor pulled out the rope and tied Fenrir up with it. But Fenrir only laughed.

'Ha!' he said. 'Do you think you can tie me up with that? I'm Fenrir, the strongest and biggest of all the wolves!' Then – very easily – he broke the big, thick rope.

Now the gods were very worried. Every day, Fenrir ate more and more, and he got bigger and bigger.

'We need to tie him up, but with a metal chain and not
a rope!' said Odin, and everybody agreed with him. So the
gods made the biggest, strongest chain they could.

'Come here!' they said to Fenrir. 'Let us tie you with this
chain, so you can always be close to us.'

Again, Fenrir did not like this, but he let the gods put
the chain around him. The gods tied the chain as tightly as
they could, but again, Fenrir only laughed.

'Ha!' he said. 'Do you think you can tie me up with this
little chain? I'm Fenrir, the strongest and biggest of all the
wolves!' He pushed his front legs, and then he pushed his
back legs and he growled, and then – *snap!* The chain broke.

Now the gods were very worried.

'We have a very dangerous animal living in Asgard with
us!' said Tyr.

'That wolf is dangerous for all of us,' said Freyja.

'You're right,' said Odin. 'We must tie him up. And this time we'll make the strongest chain of all!'

'What is that going to be?' asked Thor. 'Fenrir can break rope and metal chains easily!'

'What is the biggest and strongest thing of all?' asked Odin. 'What can never be broken?'

'I don't know,' said Thor.

'A mountain?' said Balder.

'Exactly!' said Odin. 'We'll make a big, strong chain from a mountain!'

So the gods made a chain out of a mountain, a chain of stone. When the chain was ready, the gods asked Fenrir to come to them, but Fenrir would not.

'You're going to try to tie me up again, aren't you?' he said. 'I know what you're like!'

'No!' said Odin. 'We know you're the strongest and biggest of all the wolves. So we have made a chain out of a mountain, because we want to see how strong you are!'

'Yes!' said Freyja. 'We want to see you break this chain!'

Fenrir did not like this, but he wanted the gods to see how strong he was. 'How do I know this isn't a trick?' he asked them.

This was a good question, and the gods thought hard.

'I know what we'll do,' said Odin. 'To show you this isn't a trick, we'll put the chain on you, and one of the gods will put his hand in your mouth. If you can't break the chain, then you can bite off the hand of the god!' This was a dangerous thing to say. If a god only had one hand, he could not hold a sword. If a god could not hold a sword, he would not be a strong god.

'Very well, then,' said Fenrir. 'Which god will put his hand in my mouth?' Then he laughed, because he knew this was a difficult thing for a god to do.

The gods all looked at each other. None of the gods wanted to lose a hand. The gods all looked at the big, strong teeth of the wolf.

Only Tyr came forward. Tyr was the bravest of the gods.

'I will!' he said. 'I'll put my hand in your mouth, and if you can't break this chain, you can bite off my hand!'

'Very well!' said Fenrir. 'Then let's start right now!' He laughed again.

Fenrir opened his mouth, and Tyr put his hand between the wolf's strong teeth. The gods took the big chain, made out of mountain, and tied it around the wolf.

Fenrir pushed. Fenrir pulled. Fenrir growled, then pushed and pulled again, trying to move his legs as hard as he could. He became more and more angry, and tried harder and harder. But it was no good – the wolf could not break the chain.

After an hour of trying to break the chain, his long teeth closed on Tyr's hand. Tyr did not even cry out in pain – but he knew he had lost his hand. From now on, he would never be as strong again.

Fenrir the wolf still lives in Asgard, tied up with a chain made out of stone. He is still a very, very angry wolf, waiting for a chance to escape.

2

The Story of Thrym

One morning, Thor woke up and could not find his hammer Mjollnir. Mjollnir was very important to Thor. With his hammer, he made the thunder and the lightning. Mjollnir the hammer made Thor as strong as a hundred men.

The gods took the big chain, made out of mountain,
and tied it around the wolf.

Thor looked under his bed, but it was not there. He looked in the room where he had his swords and axes and helmets, but it was not there. He looked in every one of the five hundred rooms of his palace Bilskirnir, but it was not there. There was no sign at all of Mjollnir, his magic hammer.

At first, Thor did not get worried. Thor was not the type of god who worried. Instead, Thor got angry, quickly. And when he could not find Mjollnir, he got very angry, very quickly. 'Where is it?' he shouted. 'Where's Mjollnir?'

Without Mjollnir, Thor could not make the thunder and lightning. Without Mjollnir, Thor was not the strongest of the gods.

Then, slowly, an idea came into his head: Loki! Loki was always playing tricks and jokes on the other gods. 'I know what's happening!' he thought to himself. 'I'm sure that Loki has taken my hammer for a joke!' Now, he got even more angry.

'Loki!' he shouted. 'Where are you? And what have you done with my hammer?'

Loki appeared. 'I have no idea!' he said.

'I don't believe you,' said Thor. 'You're playing a trick on me, aren't you? Where's my hammer Mjollnir? If you don't tell me, I'll ...'

But Thor did not have time to finish his sentence. Loki did not like it when Thor was angry.

'I promise I don't know!' said Loki quickly. 'It's not me! I'm not playing a joke this time!'

'Then this is very serious,' said Thor. 'If the giants have taken Mjollnir, they can get into Asgard and attack our city of the gods!'

'You're right,' said Loki. 'We need to do something.' So Loki came up with a plan.

'Here's what I'll do,' he said. 'I'll borrow Freyja's falcon skin, and with that, I can pretend to be a bird! I'll fly all around the world and look for the hammer.'

'Very well,' said Thor. 'Off you go – and be quick!'

———

Loki took the goddess's magic falcon skin and when he put it on, he became a bird – a large falcon. He flew all around Asgard and Midgard looking for the hammer. But he did not find anything. Then he went to Jotunheim, where the giants lived, and there he saw the king of the giants – Thrym. Thrym was looking very happy. He was smiling, and singing a little song to himself.

Loki took off the falcon skin, and became himself again.

'So,' Loki asked the giant. 'Where is it?'

'Where is what?' replied Thrym.

'You know what I'm talking about,' said Loki. 'Where is Mjollnir, the magic hammer you've taken from Thor!'

The giant told the truth. 'Ha!' he laughed. 'Yes! It's true. I took the hammer from Thor while he was fast asleep! He didn't see a thing! He's not very clever for a god, is he?'

'It's ours!' said Loki, 'Return it to us! Right now!'

'No way!' replied Thrym.

'If you don't give it to us at once, the gods will attack you!' said Loki angrily.

'You know that you can't fight against me if I have the hammer Mjollnir!' said Thrym. 'I will be much stronger – I will win!'

Loki said nothing. He knew that Thrym was right. 'Very well, then,' he said. 'I have an idea. Listen, if we give you something else, then will you give us Mjollnir?'

'Hmmm …' said Thrym. 'That's not a bad idea. After all, it's not Mjollnir that I want …'

'No?' asked Loki. 'What is it that you want?'

'The goddess Freyja! She's the most beautiful woman I've ever seen,' said Thrym. 'I want to marry the goddess Freyja!'

'So,' said Loki, 'If you can marry Freyja, will you give us the hammer?'

'Exactly right!' said Thrym.

'I'll see what I can do,' said Loki, and flew off, to return to Asgard.

———

'Not a chance!' said Freyja. 'No way!'

'Please!' said Loki, and all the other gods with him. 'If you marry Thrym, he'll give us the hammer, and the giants won't attack Asgard.'

But Freyja did not want to hear of it. 'There's no way I'm going to marry an ugly, old giant only to make all of you happy,' she shouted.

It was impossible. Even though the gods asked and asked, Freyja simply refused to marry the giant Thrym.

'She's right,' said Odin, after a long time. 'We'll have to think of another plan. What can we do?'

The gods all thought hard for a long time, until Loki had an idea. 'I know!' he said. 'Why doesn't Thor marry Thrym?'

'What!?' said all the other gods. 'What are you talking about?'

'Thrym the giant wants to marry the most beautiful woman there is – not a big man with a beard like Thor!' said Odin.

'That's true,' said Loki, 'But listen – we know that giants are not very intelligent …'

'That's true,' said Odin.

'And Thrym is a very stupid giant,' continued Loki.

'That's true!' said the other gods.

'So what we do is this: we put a wedding dress on Thor, and a bride's veil so Thrym can't see his face,' said Loki. 'Then we go to Jotunheim, and tell him Thor is Freyja!'

The other gods all laughed at the idea, but they liked it. 'Yes!' they said. 'This could work!'

'Then when Thrym gives us Mjollnir,' Loki said, 'We take it quickly, and run away!'

The next day, the gods all laughed again when they saw Thor wearing a wedding dress and bride's veil to cover his red hair and big beard. They laughed even more when he put on Freyja's beautiful necklace.

'That's not a beautiful bride!' said Balder, 'Anyone can see that's a man wearing a wedding dress!'

'That's not important,' said Odin. 'That giant is so stupid, he'll never see!'

Thor was very angry. 'I'm not going to do this!' he shouted. 'This is stupid!' He started to take off the veil from his face.

'Listen, my son,' said Odin to Thor. 'If you don't do this, it means the giants have Mjollnir. And you know what could happen if they come and fight us in Asgard with that magic hammer!'

Thor was angry, but he knew his father was right. It was too dangerous. He had to say 'yes' to Loki's plan – and let all the other gods laugh at him.

Loki and Thor (pretending to be the beautiful goddess Freyja) went to Jotunheim where the giant Thrym lived. As soon as Thrym saw the bride, he was very happy. 'My goodness!' he said. 'She's very tall!'

'That's true,' said Loki. 'Goddesses are very tall!'

'Can I see her face?' asked Thrym.

'No!' said Loki. 'The bride cannot take off her veil until after the wedding!'

'Oh, of course,' said Thrym. 'But can I hear her speak? I want to hear her say words of love to me!'

'No, you can't!' said Loki. 'The bride will only talk to you after the wedding.'

*The gods all laughed again when they saw
Thor wearing a wedding dress and a bride's veil.*

'Very well then,' said Thrym. 'Let's sit down now, and have the wedding dinner. After the dinner, we'll get married!'

They all sat down at a big table with lots of food on it. Thor was famous because of how much he ate – and even though he was wearing a wedding dress and a bride's veil, it did not stop him eating. First, he ate a cow. Then he ate twelve fish. Then he ate all the rest of the food on the table.

'Goodness!' said Thrym. 'She's very hungry!'

'That's because she's thinking about the wedding so much – she's forgotten to eat!' said Loki. 'She hasn't eaten anything for over a week! But now she's seen you, she's hungry again!'

Thor ate lots, but under the veil, he was very angry. 'I don't like this at all!' he whispered to Loki, and he started to take off the veil.

'No!' shouted Loki, and pulled the veil on to Thor's face again. But Thrym saw Thor's eyes.

'My goodness!' he said. 'She has very red eyes! I thought Freyja had beautiful, blue eyes.'

'That's because the bride is thinking so much about the wedding! She hasn't slept for three nights!' said Loki.

'I understand,' said Thrym. 'So, now we have eaten, let's get married!'

'Very well,' said Loki. 'But first – remember your promise! You must return the hammer Mjollnir to us!'

'Of course!' said the giant. He took out the big magic hammer and put it on the table.

As soon as Thor saw his hammer again, he could not stop himself. He jumped up, took off the bride's veil, took his hammer and laughed.

'Ha!' he said to Thrym. 'Surprised now, are you?' He lifted the hammer, and hit the giant on the head with it. 'And don't try that again!' Thor shouted to Thrym.

Then Thor and Loki returned to Asgard with the hammer Mjollnir.

'Don't tell anyone that I wore a wedding dress!' said Thor to Loki. 'I looked stupid!'

'Ha!' laughed Loki. 'Sometimes, Thor, you are stupid! But not as stupid as that giant!'

3
___

The Brisingamen Necklace

Freyja was the most beautiful of all the gods and goddesses. She was very tall, with long, blonde hair and big, blue eyes. She was the goddess of love and beauty. People in the Viking world thought that Freyja helped their flowers and plants to grow in the summer.

Freyja was a good woman, but she had one problem – she was very greedy. She was not greedy for food, but for beautiful objects. She loved diamonds and pearls – all types of jewels. She loved rings and necklaces – all types of jewellery. Freyja loved anything gold or silver. She had hundreds of gold necklaces and diamond rings, but she always wanted more.

Freyja had all of the most beautiful jewellery in Asgard, but she knew that in the other worlds there was more jewellery. Sometimes she visited Midgard to see if the humans who lived there had any beautiful jewellery for her.

'More, more, more!' she thought one day. 'I'm going to go down to Midgard, to see if there's more jewellery for me!'

But Loki – who knew everything about all the gods and goddesses – was watching her. 'I know what Freyja is doing,' he thought. 'She's going down to Midgard to see if there's any beautiful jewellery for her there.'

Loki decided to put on his magic cloak and follow her to Midgard. When Loki put on his magic cloak he was invisible. No one could see him, not even another god. 'Perhaps I can play a trick on her!' he thought.

Freyja went out and crossed the Bifrost bridge into Midgard. She looked around all the towns and cities in Midgard, but she did not find anything she liked.

All the time, Loki was following her in his magic cloak, but she did not know.

'How disappointing!' thought Freyja. 'It's very late now – but … there's somewhere else I can go …'

Loki was interested. 'Where is Freyja going now?' he thought. 'It's dark, and everyone is asleep.'

Freyja walked and walked and walked. Loki followed her for a long way. She went away from all of the human towns and cities in Midgard, until she arrived in Svartalfheim, the place where the dark elves lived.

The dark elves were famous because they were very good at making swords and axes. They also made very beautiful jewellery. Freyja loved the dark elves' jewellery, but she did not like the dark elves. The dark elves were very greedy people. They were even more greedy than Freyja. The dark elves always wanted money, lots of money.

'Of course!' thought Loki as he followed Freyja into Svartalfheim. 'The dark elves only work at night. They can't come out in the light of the day.'

Freyja watched what the dark elves were making. It was a beautiful necklace. The necklace was made of silver – silver as bright as the moon. In the silver, the dark elves were putting lots of diamonds – diamonds as shiny as the stars at night.

'That is the most beautiful piece of jewellery I've ever seen,' thought Freyja. 'I want it!'

Loki, who was still invisible, watched Freyja. He saw her looking at the necklace. He knew she wanted it.

The dark elves were not surprised to see the goddess Freyja. They knew she liked their jewellery a lot.

'Ha!' they laughed at her. 'Do you want to take this beautiful necklace we've made,' they said.

'Well,' said Freyja. 'I might be interested ...' Freyja thought that if the elves saw how much she wanted the necklace, they would ask a very high price.

'Let us tell you about this necklace,' said one of the elves. 'This is a very special necklace. Its name is Brisingamen.'

'It's made of the best silver in the world!' said another elf.

'Yes,' said the first elf. 'This silver is even better than the silver in Asgard!' He showed the necklace to Freyja. 'See?' he said. 'Look how it shines!'

'There are a hundred diamonds in this necklace,' said the other elf. 'It's very valuable!'

Freyja looked at the diamonds. Then she looked at the silver. She wanted the beautiful necklace very much. 'I must have it!' she thought.

'You say it's valuable,' she said to the elves. 'How much does it cost?'

'Cost?' asked the first elf, and then he laughed. 'My lady Freyja, this necklace has no *cost*.'

'What do you mean?' asked Freyja.

'This necklace is so valuable, it can't be sold for money,' he said.

'That's ridiculous!' said Freyja. 'I'm a goddess, and I can buy anything I want! I'll give you gold, silver ...'

'We don't need gold,' said the elf.

'Or silver,' said the second elf.

'No,' said the first elf, 'We want something more valuable than gold or silver.'

'Oh?' said Freyja. 'What is more valuable than gold or silver?'

'My lady,' said the elf quietly. 'All we want, is one kiss, from you.'

'You want me to kiss you?' asked Freyja. She was very surprised. She was a goddess. A goddess did not kiss the ugly, greedy dark elves, especially Freyja, the most beautiful goddess.

Loki was watching everything happen. 'Now this is interesting!' he thought. 'Let's see if Freyja will kiss those elves! I know the other gods won't be happy if Freyja kisses an elf.'

Freyja thought hard for a long time. She did not want to kiss the elves, but she wanted the necklace very much. She thought some more. And then she decided.

'Very well,' she said. 'I'll give each of you one kiss, and one kiss only. Then you'll give me the Brisingamen necklace, and I'll return to Asgard. Yes?'

'Yes!' said the elves.

Freyja did not like it, but she closed her eyes and kissed each of the elves, just once, on their cheeks.

'Done!' she said. 'Now give me the necklace!'

The elves gave Freyja the necklace. She put it on, and it made her look even more beautiful. Before it was day, she left. She was very happy as she went back to Asgard.

Loki saw all this happen. 'I'm going to play a trick on her!' he thought, as he followed her home.

When Freyja returned to Asgard, she did not want to tell anyone about the necklace. She was worried Odin

would know she kissed the dark elves. She wanted to show everyone the necklace, but knew it was better to hide it.

Loki wanted to make trouble, so he went to see Odin. 'Have you seen Freyja's beautiful new necklace?' he asked Odin.

'No!' said Odin. 'I'm surprised. I'm the chief god. Usually, Freyja shows me first when she has some new jewellery. It happens quite often …'

'Why do you think she hasn't shown you her new necklace?' asked Loki.

'I don't know,' said Odin. This made Odin angry. Odin was the most intelligent of the gods, but this time, he really did not know.

'Then let me tell you,' said Loki. 'Freyja got her new necklace from the dark elves!'

'What!' shouted Odin. Odin did not like the dark elves. They were good at making swords, but he thought they were bad, greedy people. 'How much did she pay the dark elves for this necklace?' he asked.

'Let me tell you,' said Loki again. 'She didn't give them any money.'

'What?' asked Odin. 'Was this necklace free? I don't believe it! I know how greedy the dark elves are!'

'No, it wasn't free,' said Loki. 'She paid a price more than money.'

'More than money? I don't understand. What are you talking about?' asked Odin.

'She gave the elves a kiss,' said Loki.

Odin was very angry. He did not want a goddess kissing the dark elves. 'How do you know this?' he asked Loki.

'I made myself invisible, and followed her,' said Loki. 'It's all true!'

'Well then,' said Odin. 'She can't have this necklace! It's not right. We must take it from her. Loki – I'm telling you to take the necklace away from Freyja!'

'Very well,' said Loki. 'I'll try.'

———

That night, while Freyja was asleep, Loki changed himself into a fly. He flew through the keyhole in Freyja's locked bedroom door and bit Freyja on the cheek. Freyja woke up. 'Oh! It's just a fly,' she said, then she turned and went back to sleep.

Now Loki could see the Brisingamen necklace. There it was, beautiful and shining, on the goddess's neck. He changed himself into a man again, and very quietly, without waking her, he took the necklace from Freyja. Then he took it to Odin.

———

When Freyja woke up the next morning, she was very surprised. 'Where is my necklace?' she shouted. 'Where

is beautiful Brisingamen?' She started to cry. 'I've lost the most beautiful necklace!' Then she started to become angry. 'Loki has something to do with this,' she thought. 'He's playing a trick on me!'

She got up and went to look for Loki, but she could not find him. Instead, she met Odin.

'What's the matter, Freyja?' asked Odin. He could see she was angry.

'I'm looking for Loki,' she said.

'Why?' asked Odin.

'He's taken something from me,' she said. 'He's playing one of his tricks on me.'

'I see,' said Odin. 'Is it, perhaps, *this* that you are looking for?' And he held up the Brisingamen necklace.

'Oh!' said Freyja. She was happy to see her necklace again, but she was worried because now Odin had it. She knew Odin would be very angry. 'Yes! That's it. My beautiful new necklace!'

'Where did it come from?' asked Odin.

'Oh, well, erm …' said Freyja, because she knew she could not tell Odin that it came from the dark elves.

'Let me look at this necklace,' said Odin. 'It's very, very beautiful. Such shiny silver. Lots of diamonds! There's only one place this necklace has come from,' he said. 'The dark elves!'

'Yes,' said Freyja. 'It's true.' She knew she could not lie to Odin. 'It came from the dark elves.'

'And how much did you pay the dark elves for this beautiful necklace?' asked Odin. 'I know they're very greedy.'

'I didn't give them money,' she said.

'Oh no?' asked Odin slowly. 'Then how did you pay them?'

Freyja knew she had to tell the truth. 'I paid them with a kiss. Three kisses,' she said.

'I thought so,' said Odin. 'All the time, Loki was following you. He was invisible. He took the necklace and gave it to me.' Odin was very angry. 'We gods do not like the dark elves. They're greedy people.'

'That's true, I know,' said Freyja. 'But I wanted the necklace so much. Please let me have it!'

'I'm very angry about this,' said Odin. 'But I'll give you the necklace …'

'Yes!' said Freyja.

'But only if …' said Odin.

'If what?' she asked.

'If you start a war,' said Odin.

'Start a war?' asked Freyja. 'Why?'

'Because I'm the god of war and battles. And when I'm angry, I want to start a new war. You will start a war, in Midgard, between two kings. And every time a man dies in the war, you will make him live again. This way, the war will continue forever!' said Odin.

'But that's a terrible thing!' replied Freyja.

'Yes, it is,' said Odin. 'But you've done a terrible thing. Do you want the necklace? Will you start the war?'

Freyja thought very hard, but only for a moment. She was greedy too, and she knew what she wanted.

'Very well,' she said. 'Yes, I'll start a war in Midgard. Now give me Brisingamen!'

Odin gave Freyja the necklace, and then she went down to Midgard again. But this time, she was not looking for jewellery, she was going to start a terrible war.

Sometimes, when they were angry, the Viking gods did terrible things.

4

Sigurd and Sigrdrifa

There was a big mountain. And around the top of the mountain there was a ring of fire. The fire burned strongly. It was impossible to see the top of the mountain, because of the ring of fire around it.

One day, a warrior called Sigurd was out riding. He was a long way from home, and did not know where he was. He saw the mountain, and the strong light at the top.

'What's that light at the top of the mountain?' he thought. So, with his horse, he went up the mountain to find out.

It was impossible to see the top of the mountain,
because of the ring of fire around it.

When he got near the top of the mountain he found the big fire burning. It was very hot, and difficult to see. His horse was afraid, but he was not. He went as near as he could to the fire, to see what was behind it. The fire was very strong, but through it he could see a great hall on top of the mountain. He was very interested.

'What's that hall on top of the mountain, behind this big fire?' he thought. There was only one way to find out. 'I'll have to pass through the fire,' he thought.

He talked to his horse, telling it not to be afraid. Then they ran as fast as they could into the fire. The fire was so hot it started to burn Sigurd's helmet, and his horse's feet. His horse began to stop – it could not continue. But Sigurd would not stop. He pushed his horse through the fire, running as fast as they could. It was very difficult. But Sigurd was a brave man, so brave he could pass through the fire. On and on they ran, until they came to the end of the fire.

Sigurd and his horse stopped and Sigurd looked up. He could now see the great hall at the top of the mountain clearly. It looked like a palace.

'I must find out what is in that hall, and why this ring of fire is around it,' he thought. He continued to walk to the top of the mountain until he reached the hall.

The doors of the hall were very big, and Sigurd had to push hard to open them. 'Nobody has opened these doors for a long time,' he thought as he pushed.

Inside, the hall was nearly empty. There was only one thing in the hall: a bed. And on the bed lay a warrior, wearing armour and a helmet. Sigurd looked at the warrior carefully. He could not see a face, because the helmet covered the warrior's head.

'Who's this warrior?' thought Sigurd. 'Is he dead or only sleeping? And why is he here in this great hall, circled by fire?' He pulled the helmet from the warrior and was surprised to find no man there, but a woman asleep. She was a very beautiful woman.

'She looks like the goddess Freyja,' thought Sigurd.

As Sigurd thought this, the woman opened her eyes and woke up. Sigurd was very surprised. 'Who are you?' he asked. 'Why are you here in this great hall? And why are you dressed like a warrior and circled by a ring of fire?'

'My name is Sigrdrifa,' she said, 'I'm a valkyrie. The valkyries are women warriors. We work for Odin, chief of the gods. When a warrior dies in battle, we take them to Valhalla, where they will live with Odin.'

'But why are you here?' said Sigurd again.

'Let me tell you the story,' she said. 'Because Freyja took the Brisingamen necklace from the dark elves, Odin made her start a war in Midgard. This war went on for a long time.

Many people thought it would go on forever. After some time, men in Midgard were tired of the war, and Odin knew it had to finish. He promised one of the kings that he would win. But that king was a bad king. I didn't want him to win. So I stopped helping Odin, and helped the other king to win a great battle. Odin was very angry with me.'

'What did he do?' asked Sigurd.

'He told me I could no longer be a valkyrie,' said Sigrdrifa, 'And that from now on I would be an ordinary woman. "You will live and die like any other woman," he said to me. "And you must marry."'

'Did you get married?' asked Sigurd.

'No,' she said. 'I didn't. I told Odin that I would only marry a man who knows no fear. So Odin was even more angry. He sent me to this place, and made me sleep. Then he put a circle of fire around the mountain so no one would find me.'

'But I found you,' said Sigurd.

'Yes,' said Sigrdrifa. 'You did. What's your name?'

'My name is Sigurd.'

'And you came through the ring of fire?' asked Sigrdrifa.

'Yes, I did,' replied Sigurd.

'Then you're a brave man,' she said.

'Thank you,' he said.

'But you're more than just a brave man,' she continued. 'You're a man who knows no fear. Is that true?'

'Yes, it's true,' said Sigurd. 'I'm afraid of nothing.'

'Then you're the man,' said Sigrdrifa. 'Marry me, and then we can leave this place.'

Sigurd and Sigrdrifa walked out of the hall, and the ring of fire was gone.

5

The Story of Alvis

Alvis was a dark elf. Nobody liked the dark elves. They were greedy people, and very unfriendly. But Alvis did not think this. 'A dark elf is as good as any other man,' he said to the other dark elves. 'Or a god!'

The other elves laughed at him. 'We're greedy people,' they said. 'And unfriendly. We like being greedy and unfriendly!' They all laughed more.

'That's true,' said Alvis. 'But I'll show you that even if I am a dark elf, I can marry the daughter of a god!'

'The daughter of a god!' said the other elves. 'Who?'

'I'm going to marry Thor's daughter, Thrud,' he said.

'You're going to marry Thrud!' said the dark elves. 'That's impossible! How can you do that?'

'I'll show you!' said Alvis. He waited until it was dark (because dark elves only go out at night), crossed the Bifrost bridge and went up into Asgard. As soon as he was in Asgard, a big man stopped him.

'Where are you going?' the man asked him. 'We don't like dark elves here in Asgard.'

Alvis was not worried, or afraid. He thought that this man couldn't be a god. This man was very big and strong, that was true. But he had a big, red beard and did not look very intelligent. He looked like a farmer.

'I'm going to meet Thor,' said Alvis.

'Oh really?' said the man. 'And why do you want to meet Thor?' he asked.

'I'm going to marry his daughter, Thrud,' said Alvis. 'I've come up here so I can take her home with me.'

What Alvis did not know was that this farmer was really

Thor himself. Usually, Thor was not very intelligent, and he became angry very quickly. But today, Thor did not become angry. This time, Thor decided to be intelligent like his father Odin. 'This little elf doesn't know who I am,' thought Thor. 'I can have some fun with him ...'

'What's your name?' Thor asked the elf.

'My name is Alvis! I'm a dark elf!' he said.

'I thought so,' said Thor. 'People don't like dark elves. Dark elves are greedy and unfriendly.'

''That's true,' said Alvis. 'But I'll show that we can marry the daughters of gods.'

'So you want to marry Thrud, daughter of Thor?' asked the god.

'That's right,' replied the elf.

'But you're not very handsome, are you?' asked Thor. 'You're a dark elf!'

'That's also true. But – as a dark elf – I'm very good at making swords and axes, and jewellery!' said Alvis.

'That's true,' replied Thor.

'And I have a house in a cave!' said the elf.

'A house in a cave!' said Thor. 'Do you think a father will be happy if he knows his daughter has a house in a cave?'

'It's a very nice cave,' said the elf.

'A father should always decide who his daughter marries,' said Thor.

'That's true,' said Alvis. 'That's why I am going to meet Thor right now. What's your name, by the way?'

'Ha!' said Thor. He wanted to be angry, but he stopped himself. Instead he laughed. 'My name is Thor!' he shouted. 'That's right – I am Thor!'

'Oh,' said Alvis. He was very surprised. He did not think this fat man with a big beard looked like Thor at all. 'I thought you were a farmer,' he said.

Thor stopped himself from becoming angry again. 'A farmer!' he thought. 'This stupid elf thought I was a farmer! I'll show him.' He remembered that he wanted to be intelligent this time.

'I'm happy that I met you,' said Alvis. 'Now it's easy for me. I want to marry your daughter Thrud!'

'It's not that easy,' said Thor. 'Listen, here's what we'll do. I'll ask you some questions, and if you can answer them, you can marry my daughter. Yes?'

'Yes!' said Alvis. Alvis thought Thor was not very intelligent. It would be easy to answer his questions.

'I want to know if you're an intelligent man,' said Thor, 'So here's my first question for you.'

'Go on!' said Alvis.

'What is it that we live in?' asked Thor.

Alvis thought the answer might be 'a house'. But then he

thought that he lived in a cave, not a house, and Thor lived in a great hall, not a house.

'No,' he thought. 'It's something more than a house.' So he said, 'It has many names. Some people call it Earth, or the world. We live in all of Yggdrasil, I in Svartalfheim, and you in Asgard.'

'That's true,' said Thor. 'Very good. Now, what is it that covers us all?'

Alvis had to think about this one. He thought about the roof of his cave and Thor's great hall, but it was not that. 'It's the roof of the world,' he said. 'The sky! The sky goes all around us, and covers every one of us.'

'A good answer,' said Thor. 'Now for my next question: what is the night sun?'

Alvis had to think hard about this one. 'There's no sun at night,' he thought to himself. 'And I've never seen the sun, because the sun kills dark elves. The only thing I know is … of course!' He looked at Thor and said, 'What makes light in the night? The moon!'

'Well done,' said Thor. 'And what is the name for the fire that burns in the sky?'

This was an easy one. 'I've never seen it,' said Alvis, 'But I know that men call it the sun!'

'Yes,' said Thor, still thinking carefully. 'What can make water fly?'

This was a difficult one. Alvis had to think hard.

'Come on!' said Thor. 'Hurry up! I can't wait all night for your answer.'

'I know!' said Alvis. 'The clouds! The clouds hold water in the sky, and then it rains …'

'Good answer,' said Thor. 'Here's another question. What moves through every country, everyone knows it, but no one ever sees it?'

This was a difficult question. Alvis knew some of the gods could become invisible. But when a god was invisible, not everyone knew that. Rivers moved through every country, but people could see rivers. Then he understood. 'I know!' he said, 'The wind!'

'A good answer,' said Thor. 'Here's another question – what is the water that nobody can drink?'

This was easy. 'The sea!' said Alvis.

'True,' said Thor. It was becoming difficult for Thor to think of more questions, but he waited. He needed to wait. 'Very well,' he said after some time. 'What is the thing we all have in our homes which helps us, but is so dangerous it can kill us?'

At first, Alvis was going to say 'a sword', but then he thought that not everyone has a sword in their homes. He thought for a long time before he knew the answer. 'Fire!' he said.

'Right again,' said Thor. 'I can see that you're intelligent ... for an elf!' Thor looked up. The night was coming to an end. 'What is the dark that helps men and gods sleep?' he asked.

'Easy!' thought Alvis. 'The night!' he said.

Thor laughed. 'Yes,' he said, 'And what is its opposite?'

Only then did Alvis understand the trick Thor was playing on him. He looked up. The night was ending, and the sun was coming up. 'Oh no,' he thought. 'I can't see the sun. If I see the sun I will die!'

Thor laughed again. 'Go on Alvis! Do you know the name for it?'

'Oh yes,' said Alvis, 'but it's too late for me now ... now that I've seen – the day!'

As Alvis said the word, the sun came up into Asgard, and when Alvis saw it he became a stone.

Some people say that if you go to the place where Thor met the dark elf Alvis, you can still see a small stone there, a stone still waiting to marry the god's daughter. He will wait for a long time. For once, Thor was clever!

6

Thor and the Giants

It was the beginning of the summer, and Thor was bored.

'I'm bored!' he said to Loki.

'But this is Asgard!' said Loki. 'It's the most beautiful place in all of Yggdrasil.'

'Yes, but it's quiet here,' replied Thor. 'Too quiet.'

'So what do you want to do?' asked Loki.

'I think I should go and fight some giants!' he said. 'There are too many giants.'

'But if the giants are quiet, why don't we leave them alone?' asked Loki.

'Sooner or later they'll make trouble for us!' said Thor.

Loki did not think this was a good idea, but he knew that when Thor decided something it was impossible to stop him. 'Very well, then,' he said. 'But remember this, Thor – you need to be clever to fight giants. And you're not always very intelligent, are you?'

'That's ridiculous!' replied Thor. 'I was clever when I stopped the dark elf Alvis from marrying my daughter.'

'Yes, that's true,' said Loki. 'But that doesn't happen often. If you're going to fight giants, then I think I should come with you!'

'I'm not sure about that, Loki,' replied Thor. 'You might start playing some of your tricks.'

'I promise I won't play any tricks,' said Loki.

'Very well then!' said Thor. 'Together we'll be able to fight all the giants! Come on. Let's go! Right now!'

'It's late now,' said Loki. 'We should wait until early tomorrow. Then we'll have a day to travel to the country of the giants.'

Thor agreed, and the next morning they took Thor's chariot and put the two goats Tanngrisnir and Tanngnjóstr in front of it. Thor's two goats were very special: they were very strong goats, so they could pull Thor's chariot through the sky. But at the end of each day, Thor killed and ate them. The next day, they came back to life.

Tanngrisnir and Tanngnjóstr pulled Thor and Loki across the sky. They flew above Asgard, and looked down.

'Look how beautiful it is!' said Loki.

'Yes, it is,' said Thor. 'But I want to go and fight some giants! Come on, quick!' he shouted to the goats. They travelled all day, but when night came, they were still in Midgard, the country of the humans.

'We should stop here for the night,' said Loki.

'Can't we continue?' asked Thor. 'I want to *see* some giants, at least!'

'The goats are getting tired now,' replied Loki. 'Look, there's a farmhouse! We can stop there.'

Thor stopped the chariot on the ground, next to the farmhouse. The house was very old. It looked very poor.

'Does anyone live in this place?' asked Thor.

'I don't think so,' said Loki. 'But knock on the door and see.'

Thor knocked on the door of the old farmhouse. He was so strong he nearly broke the old door. To their surprise, a woman came out.

'Who are you, and what do you want?' she asked.

'We're the gods Thor and Loki!' said Thor. 'And we want a place to stay for the night.'

The woman looked very surprised. She went back inside, then came out with her husband, the farmer. 'Who are you, and what do you want?' asked the farmer.

'Don't get angry!' said Loki to Thor.

'I've just said – we're the gods Thor and Loki, and we want a place to stay for the night!' Thor said again.

'Of course you can stay here for the night,' said the farmer. 'But I'm afraid we have very little food, and no meat.'

'No meat?' said Thor. 'Don't worry about that – I have my two goats, Tanngrisnir and Tanngnjóstr. I'll kill them now, and then we can all eat!'

They went inside the farmhouse and started a fire. Thor killed his goats, and they cooked them on the fire.

'This is our son, Thialfi,' said the farmer. 'Can he eat with us too?'

'Of course,' said Thor. 'There's lots of meat from the goats you can eat – but don't eat any of the bones!'

They were all very hungry, and ate both of the goats. Then they were all tired, so they went to bed. But the farmer's son, Thialfi, was still very hungry. When everyone was asleep, he got up and took a leg bone from one of the goats. There was a lot of meat on the bone, so Thialfi put it under his bed.

'I'll eat this later,' he thought. 'No one will know.'

That night, they all slept very well.

—

The next morning, Thor used his hammer Mjollnir to bring the goats back to life. The goats lived again, but Thor saw that one of them could not walk properly. 'Tanngrisnir has no bone in his back leg,' said Thor. 'I told you not to eat the bones, only the meat! That is why my goat Tanngrisnir has no bone in his back leg!'

Thor was becoming very angry now, and the farmer, his wife and his son were very worried.

'I didn't eat the bone!' said the farmer.

'I didn't eat the bone,' said the farmer's wife.

'Loki – is this one of your tricks?' asked Thor.

'No, it isn't,' replied Loki. 'I didn't eat the bone.'

Then very quietly, Thialfi said, 'It was me. I ate the bone!'

Thor was angry, and lifted up his hammer to hit Thialfi.

'No! Stop!' said Loki. 'Don't hit him! He's only a poor, hungry boy. I've got a better idea.'

'What's that?' asked Thor.

'Because the boy ate the bone, and we told him not to, he must come with us on our journey,' said Loki. 'He can help us fight the giants!'

'But he's only a boy,' said Thor. 'He can't help us!'

'I'm not sure,' said Loki. 'I think a human might be able to help us.'

'Very well then,' said Thor. 'Thialfi, you will come with us!'

The farmer and his wife were sad to see their son leave, but knew they could not stop Thor.

So Thor, Loki and Thialfi got in the chariot and flew off again. They travelled for a long time. They crossed mountains and seas, and when the day was ending, they stopped in the middle of a big forest.

'I don't like this place,' said Loki.

'What? Are you frightened?' asked Thor. 'The god Loki is frightened of the forest!'

'I'm not frightened,' said Loki. 'But we don't know where we are. And it's very dark here. Thialfi – go into the forest and see if there's a house near here.'

Thialfi was worried. He did not want to go into the dark forest on his own at night, but he knew he had to go. He walked off into the forest.

After a long time, he found a big house. It was a very unusual house. It did not have any doors or windows, for example. It only had a big space for a door.

'This house is unusual, but it's very big,' thought Thialfi. 'We can stay here tonight.' He ran back through the forest to Thor and Loki and told them about the house. The three of them went through the dark forest to sleep in the big, strange house.

In the middle of the night, there was a loud noise. It sounded like thunder.

'Is that you, Thor?' asked Loki. 'Making thunder with your hammer Mjollnir?'

'No,' replied Thor. 'I was asleep.'

'Something is not right here,' said Loki. 'Look – over there is a smaller room. I think it isn't so dangerous if we sleep in there.'

Thor, Loki and Thialfi moved from the big room to the small room, and again went to sleep. But after a few minutes, the loud noise came again. They looked around, but could see nothing, so they tried to sleep again.

Next morning they woke up and walked out of the house into the forest, and found out what the noise was. Next to the house was a giant, lying asleep on the floor of the forest. The giant made a loud sound while he slept. He was snoring.

'So that was the noise!' said Thor. 'This sleeping giant!'

They all looked at the giant. He was very big, even for a giant.

'I'll hit him with my hammer!' said Thor.

'No! Don't do that!' said Loki. 'It's more intelligent if we ask him who he is, and where there are other giants.'

'Very well,' said Thor, sadly.

They woke the giant up. When he stood up, he was taller than the trees.

'Who are you?' asked Thor.

'Skrymir,' said the giant. 'It means 'big man'.'

'I'm not surprised,' said Loki.

'I know who you are – you are Thor and you are Loki. But who's this boy?' asked Skrymir.

'That's Thialfi. He's helping us,' said Thor.

'Where are my gloves?' said Skrymir. The giant looked around, and then picked up the house.

'And so that was our house!' said Loki. They all looked at the house, and saw that it was not a house at all. It was the giant's glove! The fingers of the glove were the rooms.

'That's why it has no doors!' laughed Thialfi.

'I'm going to the country of the giants,' said Skrymir. 'Why don't you come with me?'

'I want to fight him now,' said Thor to Loki.

'Not now!' said Loki. 'He's a very big giant. We should go with him, so we can meet more giants.'

'Very well,' said Thor, sadly.

'But we have to walk there,' said the giant. 'I can't go in your chariot.'

*They all looked at the house, and saw that it was
not a house at all. It was the giant's glove!*

Thor did not like this, but Loki told him it was the best thing to do. They left the chariot and the two goats in the middle of the forest.

They walked all day through the forest. The giant walked very quickly. It was difficult to walk as fast as the giant. When evening came, they were very tired.

'Let's sleep here,' said Skrymir.

'But we have no food to eat!' said Thor.

'Oh, I've got lots of food in my bag,' said the giant. He put a bag as big as five men on the floor. 'You can have anything you want. I'm going to sleep now. Goodnight!' And the giant lay down on the floor, and went to sleep.

Thor, Loki and Thialfi were very hungry.

'There's lots of food in the giant's bag!' said Thor. 'Let's eat.'

They tried to open the bag, but it was impossible. They pulled and pulled and pulled, but the bag would not open. Thor became very angry. 'That giant has tricked us!' he shouted. 'I'm going to hit him with my hammer!'

This time, Loki could not stop Thor. Thor picked up his hammer and hit the giant on the head with it, very hard.

The giant woke up. 'I thought I felt something,' he said. 'Was that a leaf falling on my head?' Then he went back to sleep again.

Now Thor was even more angry. He picked up his hammer again, and this time hit the giant even harder.

The giant woke up again. 'I can't get any sleep tonight,' he said. 'Was that a bird on my face?' He did not wait for an answer, but went back to sleep, and started snoring again.

'There's nothing we can do,' said Loki. 'This giant is too big for us. We'll have to go to sleep hungry, and see if he takes us to the other giants tomorrow.'

50

The next morning they all woke up.

'I'm going this way,' said Skrymir the giant. 'But if you want to go to the country of the giants, it's that way. It's not far, but be careful! If you go there, you'll find giants who are bigger than me!' Then, he walked away.

Thor, Loki and Thialfi followed the giant's instructions and only an hour later, they found a very big castle. 'This is the castle of the giants!' said Thor. 'Now let's go and fight them!'

But when they arrived at the door of the giants' castle, it was closed, and they could not open it. They looked at the walls of the castle. They were very high, too high for them to climb over.

'How can we get in?' asked Thor.

Thialfi found a window. There was no glass in the window, but there were some bars in it, like the window of a prison. 'Look!' said Thialfi. 'I can go between the bars of this window.' And he climbed up and went between the bars and into the giants' castle. Loki could get between the bars as well. But Thor could not. Thor was too big.

'Help!' he said to Loki and Thialfi. 'I can't get between these bars!'

Loki and Thialfi had to pull, very hard, to make Thor get between the bars. After nearly an hour, they were all inside.

They walked into a big room which was full of giants – men and women giants, old and young giants.

'I've never seen so many giants!' said Thor.

'And these are the biggest giants I've ever seen!' said Loki.

The giants were so big they did not even see Thor, Loki and Thialfi at first. When they did see them, they only laughed.

'Hello little people!' said the biggest giant. 'I'm Utgard, king of the giants. You're Thor, aren't you?'

'Yes I am!' said Thor.

'I thought you were bigger than that,' said Utgard. 'And you're Loki!' he continued. 'But who's this?'

'I'm Thialfi,' the farmer's son said.

'Ha!' said Utgard. 'A human! So why have you all come here?'

'I have come here to fight you all!' said Thor.

'I'm sorry,' said Utgard. 'I didn't hear that. You have to speak loudly if you speak to a giant!'

'Shut up!' said Loki angrily to Thor. 'We can't fight all these giants!'

'Everyone in this castle has a special ability,' said Utgard. 'One giant is the strongest, another giant is the fastest runner, another giant is the most intelligent. To be in this castle, everybody must be the best at something. So tell me, Thor, Loki and Thialfi, what are *you* good at?'

Loki, who was very hungry, said, 'I can eat faster than anyone in this castle!'

'Ha!' laughed Utgard. 'Is that true? Then let's see.' Utgard told the other giants to bring a table of food into the room. It was a very long table, and there was lots of meat on it. Loki sat at one end of the table.

'This giant here can eat more than any other giant,' continued Utgard. Another giant sat at the other end of the table. 'Let's see if you can eat more than him!'

Loki and the giant both began to eat the meat on the table. As they ate, they moved their chairs closer to the middle of the table. Loki was very hungry, so he ate and ate and ate all the meat on the table. Soon he was sitting next to the giant in the middle of the table. But Loki only ate the meat, the giant then ate the bones of the meat as well.

'Ha!' laughed the giant. And then he ate the table as well.

'Loki,' said Utgard. 'You're the loser!'

Loki was angry, but he did not say anything.

'And what about you, human boy? What can you do?' Utgard asked Thialfi.

'I can run very fast!' said Thialfi. 'I'm the fastest runner in Midgard!'

'Is that true?' asked Utgard. 'Then let's see. Hugi is the fastest of the giants. He'll run against you.'

Thor, Loki, Thialfi and all of the giants went out of the castle into a field. Thialfi and the giant Hugi stood at one end of the field.

'When I say "*go*"', said Utgard, 'you'll both run to the other end of the field. Are you ready? Then *go*!'

Thialfi ran as fast as he could. He ran so fast his feet did not touch the floor. He ran so fast he felt he was flying. He knew he was going to win the race against the big, heavy giant. But when he arrived at the other end of the field, the giant Hugi was already there, waiting for him.

'Hello little boy!' said Hugi. It seemed Hugi only took two steps to cross the field. He did not have to run at all.

'Thialfi,' said Utgard. 'You're the loser!'

Thialfi was very angry, but he did not say anything.

'So you, Thor,' said Utgard. 'You're good at telling everyone how strong you are, but let's see what you can really do!'

'I can do many things!' said Thor.

'For example?' asked Utgard.

'Well, I can drink more than anyone else!' replied Thor.

'You can drink more than anyone else, can you?' asked Utgard. 'Then let's see!' Utgard told another giant to bring out the giants' drinking horn. The giants' drinking horn was as big as Thor himself. 'This is what the giants drink from,' said Utgard. 'Let's see if you can empty it!'

Thor stood next to the drinking horn and started to drink from it. He drank and drank as much as he could. But the level of the water in the drinking horn did not go down one little bit.

'Ha!' said Utgard. 'Is that all you can drink? Try again!'

Thor drank again from the big drinking horn. He drank and drank and drank, but this time when he finished there was more water in it than when he started.

'That might be a lot in Asgard, but it's not much in my kingdom!' said Utgard.

Thor was angry, but he did not say anything.

'Let's see what else you can do,' said Utgard. 'You think you're strong, don't you?'

'I am the strongest of all the gods!' said Thor.

54

'Look, then' said Utgard, and he pointed at a cat under a table. 'There's my little cat. Pick it up!'

Thor thought this was going to be easy. He took hold of the cat, and tried to pick it up. But even though the cat was small (for a giant's cat), Thor could not lift it. He pulled and pulled and pulled, but only one of the cat's feet left the floor. All the giants laughed at Thor. Now, he was really angry.

'Let me fight with any one of you!' he said. 'I'll show you how strong I really am!'

'You want to fight with one of us, do you?' asked Utgard. 'Very well then. Elli!' he shouted.

Elli arrived. Elli was an old woman. She was an old woman giant, but not much bigger than Thor. And she was very, very old.

'This is Elli,' said Utgard. 'She's my grandmother. Let's see if you can fight her!'

'But she's an old woman!' said Thor. 'I can't fight her!'

'I'm ready to fight you,' said Elli.

'Are you afraid?' asked Utgard.

'Of course not!' said Thor. And they started to fight. Thor tried to push Elli to the floor, but he could not. Instead, Elli picked Thor up and threw him across the room. Then she came and stood on top of him. 'I'm the winner!' she shouted. 'I'm stronger than the god Thor!'

All the giants laughed and laughed.

'Now,' said Utgard. 'I think we've seen who's the strongest here, and the biggest eater, and the fastest runner. And it's not you. So goodbye Thor, goodbye Loki and goodbye Thialfi. Go home now, and don't think you can fight with giants again! Let me show you the way home.'

Thor, Loki and Thialfi were very angry, but they did not say anything. They knew they were the losers in this competition. They followed Utgard out of the giants' castle.

Outside the castle, Utgard started to tell them something. 'I heard you were coming here,' he said. 'Skrymir told me. I was worried. I didn't want Thor and Loki to fight us.'

'What are you telling us?' asked Thor.

'You're too strong for us, I know that,' continued Utgard. 'So I used tricks to win those competitions!'

'Tricks!' shouted Thor. 'I thought it was Loki who played tricks!'

'Ha!' said Utgard. 'We giants know how to play tricks as well! While Loki was eating all that meat, but not the bones, we took the bones from the table and burned them. You were watching Loki, so you didn't see us.'

'And the running competition?' asked Thialfi.

'You're a very fast runner!' said Utgard. 'Perhaps the fastest runner in Midgard. A big, heavy giant couldn't win against you.'

'So what did you do?' asked Thialfi.

'We put Hugi's twin brother at the other end of the field,' said Utgard. 'You didn't even see!'

'And what about the drinking horn?' asked Thor.

'That drinking horn is so big because it's connected to the sea. The water you drank was the sea itself! Nobody can drink the sea!' said Utgard.

'I thought it tasted salty,' said Thor. 'And the cat?'

'That's no ordinary cat, said Utgard. 'That cat was actually Jormungand, the snake who goes around the world. He changed into a cat, because I asked him. Not even a god can pick up Jormungand!'

'And the old lady?' asked Thor.

'That was no old lady,' said Utgard. 'That lady is old age itself. And nobody, not even a god, can stop old age.'

Thor was very angry, and lifted up his hammer Mjollnir to hit Utgard, king of the giants. 'I'll kill you all!' he shouted.

'Wait!' said Utgard. 'We have used magic to win against you, that's true. But we can use magic again if we want. I will protect my kingdom from the angry gods!'

Thor brought down his hammer as hard and as quickly as he could, but it touched nothing. Utgard and the giants' castle were gone. There was nothing there. Thor, Loki and Thialfi looked around, but there was no sign of a giant or of a castle.

'I think we'll have to walk home,' said Loki. 'And next time you get bored, think of something different to do!'

Points For Understanding

The World of the Vikings' Tales

1 Where did the Viking gods live?
2 Where did the people live?
3 Where did the giants live?
4 What connected Asgard and Midgard?
5 Who was Jormungand? Where did he live?
6 Who was the chief of the gods? Where did he live?
7 Who was Odin's son? Where did he live? What did he eat?
8 Was Loki a good god or a bad god?
9 Who was the most important goddess?
10 Why were the dark elves bad? What were they good at?

1 Fenrir's Chain

1 Who were Loki's three children?
2 What did the gods do to Jormungand the snake?
3 What did the gods do to Hel?
4 Why did the gods decide to keep Fenrir in Asgard?
5 Who was Fenrir's best friend?
6 When did Fenrir get angry?
7 Why did the gods get worried? What did they decide to do?
8 What did Fenrir do to the rope?
9 What did the gods try next?
10 What did Fenrir do this time?
11 How did the gods make a very strong chain?
12 Why did Tyr put his hand in Fenrir's mouth?
13 Why was this a brave thing to do?

14 Did Fenrir break the last chain?
15 Why was Tyr not as strong at the end of the story?
16 Where does Fenrir live now? What is he waiting for?

2 The Story of Thrym

1 Why was Mjollnir so important to Thor?
2 Why did Thor think Loki took the hammer?
3 What did Loki decide to do?
4 When did Thrym take the hammer?
5 What did Thrym really want?
6 Did Freyja want to marry Thrym?
7 What did the other gods do to Thor? Why?
8 Why did the gods laugh at Thor? How did Thor feel?
9 Did Thrym know the bride was really Thor?
10 Why did Loki think the giant was stupid?

3 The Brisingamen Necklace

1 What was Freyja's problem? What did she want more of?
2 What did Loki do?
3 Why could Freyja not see Loki?
4 Where did Freyja go?
5 Why did Freyja not like the dark elves?
6 What did Freyja think about the necklace?
7 What did the elves want for the necklace?
8 Why did Freyja not want to give it to them?
9 Why did Loki tell Odin what happened?
10 What did Loki do to get the necklace?
11 Did Odin let Freyja keep the necklace?
12 What did Odin tell Freyja to do?

4 Sigurd and Sigrdrifa

1 Who was Sigurd?
2 What did he see?
3 Why was it difficult to reach the hall?
4 Who did Sigurd find in the hall?
5 Why was he surprised?
6 What is a 'valkyrie'?
7 Why did Sigrdrifa stop helping Odin?
8 Why will Sigrdrifa marry Sigurd?

5 The Story of Alvis

1 What did Alvis want to do?
2 Who did Alvis think Thor was?
3 What was different about Thor?
4 Why did Alvis think Thrud would want to marry him?
5 Why did Thor take a long time to ask Alvis all his questions?
6 Why was the last question so important?
7 What can people still find at the place where Thor met Alvis?
8 What did Thor do differently this time?

6 Thor and the Giants

1 Why did Thor want to go and fight giants?
2 Why did Loki decide to go with Thor?
3 What always happened to Thor's goats?
4 Who was Thialfi? What did he do wrong?
5 What did Loki suggest Thialfi should do?
6 Where did the three of them stop for the night?
7 Why did they not sleep well?
8 What was unusual about the 'house' they slept in?
9 Why can they not get in to the giants' castle?
10 Who was Utgard?
11 What did Loki say he could do?
12 Who won the eating competition?
13 What did Thialfi say he could do?
14 Who won the running competition?
15 What did Thor say he could do?
16 Did Thor drink all the water?
17 Was Thor stronger than the old woman?
18 How did Utgard win the competitions?

Exercises

Background Information

Choose the correct information to complete the sentences.

1 The Vikings were from *Southern Europe*/ *Scandinavia.*

2 The Vikings lived around *1000 years ago*/*500 years ago.*

3 Asgard was the part of the tree where the *gods*/*humans* lived.

4 The most important god was *Odin*/*Thor.*

5 The Vikings called the big houses where the gods lived *'palaces'*/*'halls'.*

6 *Loki*/*Thor* was Odin's son.

7 *Tyr*/*Loki* was a god who tricked people and changed shape or form.

8 Freyja was the *god*/*goddess* of love.

9 The giants and the gods were *friends*/*enemies.*

10 The *giants*/*elves* died in the light of day.

Multiple Choice

Tick the best answer.

1 Which of the following was NOT a god?
   a Thor
   b Loki
   c Thrym ✓
   d Tyr

2 Who was sent to be queen of Niflheim?
   a Freyja
   b Hel
   c Jormungand
   d Fenrir

3 Which is NOT true of Mjollnir?
   a It can be used to make thunder and lightning.
   b The gods lose it to the giants forever.
   c Thor uses it to be the strongest god.
   d It is a magic hammer.

4 What does Loki pretend to be so he can go and look for Mjollnir?
   a A bride
   b A bird
   c An elf
   d A giant

5 Which is NOT true of the dark elves?
   a They are very greedy.
   b They are good at making beautiful jewellery.
   c They work at night.
   d They live in Asgard.

6 Who was the god of war and battles?
   a Odin
   b Freyja
   c Thor
   d Loki

7 Where do warriors who die in battle go?
   a To the sea around Midgard
   b To Valhalla with Odin
   c To Niflheim
   d To Jotunheim with the giants

8 Which is true of Sigurd?
   a He is a valkyrie.
   b Odin is angry with him.
   c He is afraid of nothing.
   d He dies in a war.

9 Which is NOT true of Alvis?
   a He marries Thor's daughter.
   b He has a house in a cave.
   c He's good at making swords and jewellery.
   d He turns to stone.

10 Which animals pull Thor's chariot?
   a Wolves
   b Goats
   c Eagles
   d Horses

11 How do Thor, Loki and Thialfi get into the giants'
   castle?
   a By climbing over the walls
   b By climbing through the window bars
   c Through the open door
   d By asking the giant Skyrmir for help

12 Who was the king of the giants?
   a Thialfi
   b Alvis
   c Utgard
   d Skyrmir

Useful Phrases

Match a verb with a noun to make phrases from the stories. Then complete the sentences with the phrases.

VERB	NOUN
1 tell	a trick
2 start	the truth
3 play	a war
4 attack	questions
5 take off	a chariot
6 answer	the city
7 pull	a chain
8 break	the veil

1 Freyja has to _____*tell the truth*_____ to Odin about how she got the necklace from the elves.

2 Fenrir is so strong that he can _____ made of strong metal.

3 The gods are afraid that the giants might use Mjollnir, to _____ of the gods.

4 Loki tells Thrym, 'The bride can't _____ until after the wedding.'

5 Two cats _____ for Freyja.

6 Odin asks Freyja to _____ in Midgard.

7 Alvis, the dark elf, tries to _____ from Thor because he wants to marry his daughter.

8 The giants _____ on Thor and Loki so they can win the competitions.

65

Words from the Stories

Complete the gaps. Use each word in the box once.

> feast   helmet   jewellery   rainbow
> ~~snake~~   squirrel   sword   tears

1 Jormungand is a very big _____ *snake* _____
   which lives in the sea around Midgard.

2 Bifrost, the bridge from Asgard to Midgard, is like a
   burning _____.

3 Ratatosk is a _____ which runs up
   and down the tree, taking messages from one place to
   another.

4 There is a _____ every night in
   Valhalla where everyone sits together and eats and
   drinks a lot.

5 When she cries, Freyja cries _____ of
   gold.

6 Freyja already has many rings and necklaces, but she is
   still greedy for more beautiful _____.

7 If a god had only one hand, he could not hold a
   _____ and be a strong god.

8 Sigurd cannot see the warrior's face because it is
   covered by a _____.

Grammar: *because* and *so*

Match the sentence halves 1–8 with a–h.

1 Fenrir, the wolf, cannot break the chain   *e*

2 Thor dresses as a bride   ....

3 Freyja wants the necklace   ....

4 Sigrdrifa stops helping Odin   ....

5 Sigrdrifa asks Sigurd to marry her   ....

6 Alvis the dark elf turns to stone   ....

7 One of the goats cannot walk properly   ....

8 Utgard uses tricks and magic in the competitions   ....

a , so he can get back the magic hammer, Mjollnir, from Thrym.

b , so he becomes angry and sends her to sleep.

c , so she kisses the dark elves.

d because Thialfi eats his bone.

e , so he bites the hand of Tyr.

f because he sees the sun.

g because he knows no fear.

h because he knows the gods are too strong for the giants.

Grammar: Superlatives with present perfect

Complete the sentences with the superlative form of the adjective given and the past participle (third form) of the verb.

1 'Fenrir is _the most dangerous_ (dangerous) animal we've ever _had_ (have) in Asgard!' said Freyja.

2 'This is .... (strong) chain we've ever .... (make)!' said Odin.

3 'This is .... (beautiful) necklace I've ever .... (wear)!' said Freyja.

4 'You're .... (brave) man I've ever .... (meet)!' said Sigrdrifa.

5 'These are .... (big) giants I've ever .... (see)!' said Loki.

6 'This is .... (fast) race I've ever .... (run)!' said Thialfi.

7 'This is .... (heavy) cat I've ever .... (try) to pick up!' said Thor.

8 'Elli is .... (strong) woman I've ever .... (fight) against!' said Thor.

Grammar: Comparison

Rewrite the sentences using the word given and keeping the meaning the same.

1   Thor is not as intelligent as his father, Odin.
    more

    Odin *is more intelligent than his son, Thor.*

2   The metal chain is stronger than the rope.
    less

    The rope ....

3   Freyja is not as greedy as the dark elves.
    than

    Freyja ....

4   Gold or silver are less valuable than a kiss.
    more

    A kiss ....

5   The giant eats faster than Loki.
    than

    Loki ....

6   Loki does not eat as much as the giant.
    more

    The giant ....

7   Thor is not as strong as Elli.
    than

    Elli ....

8   Thor drinks less than the giants.
    more

    The giants ....

Grammar: First conditional

Match the sentence halves 1–8 with a–h to make a first conditional sentence. Which person says each sentence? Choose a name from the box.

Alvis   Freyja   Loki   Odin   Sigrdrifa
Thor   ~~Tyr~~   Utgard

1 If he can't break the chain,   _c_   _Tyr_

2 If I put on my magic cloak, ...

3 If I kiss these elves, ...

4 If you want to keep this necklace, ...

....

5 If I meet a man who knows no fear, ...

....

6 If you want to marry my daughter, ...

....

7 If I see the sun, ...

8 If we use magic in these competitions, ...

....

a I'll marry him.

b I'll get this beautiful necklace.

c I'll lose my hand.

d I'll become invisible and play a trick on her.

e you'll have to start a war in Midgard.

f I'll die!

g we'll be able to win against the gods.

h you'll have to answer some difficult questions.

Visit the Macmillan Readers website at
www.macmillanenglish.com/readers

*to find **FREE resources** for use in class and for independent learning. Search our **online catalogue** to buy new Readers including **audio download** and **eBook** versions.*

Here's a taste of what's available:

For the classroom:

- **Tests** for most Readers to check understanding and monitor progress
- **Worksheets** for most Readers to explore language and themes
- **Listening worksheets** to practise extensive listening
- Worksheets to help prepare for the **First (FCE) reading exam**

Additional resources for students and independent learners:

- An **online level test** to identify reading level
- **Author information sheets** to provide in-depth biographical information about our Readers authors
- **Self-study worksheets** to help track and record your reading which can be used with any Reader
- Use our **creative writing worksheets** to help you write short stories, poetry and biographies
- Write academic essays and literary criticism confidently with the help of our **academic writing worksheets**
- Have fun completing our **webquests** and **projects** and learn more about the Reader you are studying
- Go backstage and read **interviews** with **famous authors** and **actors**
- Discuss your favourite Readers at the **Book Corner Club**

Visit www.macmillanenglish.com/readers to find out more!

Macmillan Education
4 Crinan Street
London N1 9XW
A division of Macmillan Publishers Limited

Companies and representatives throughout the world

ISBN 978-0-230-46027-0
ISBN 978-0-230-46029-4 (with CD edition)

Designed by Carolyn Gibson
Illustrated by Giorgio Bacchin
Cover photograph by Getty Images/AFP

Printed and bound in Thailand

without CD edition

2019	2018	2017	2016	2015	2014
10	9	8	7	6	5	4	3	2	1

with CD edition

2019	2018	2017	2016	2015	2014
10	9	8	7	6	5	4	3	2	1